£3·25

**Question:** What is Bernard Matthews' favourite church song?
**Answer:** "All Things Bright and BOOTIFUL."

4

7

# The Winners

I'VE WON THE LADIES' KNITTING COMPETITION!

IN THE CARRIER-PIGEON CONTEST, I PIPPED THE REST!

I WAS FIRST AT FIELD-CRAFT!

I WON AT WISE-CRACKING!

THAT NIGHT...

THE WINNERS LIVE THERE! THEY MUST HAVE **TONS** OF TROPHIES WORTH STEALING!

QUIETLY DOES IT... AND WE'RE IN!

COO! LOOK AT ALL THAT **SILVER!**

SSH!

WE'LL NEVER HAVE TO WORK AGAIN, AFTER SELLIN' THIS LOT!

LET'S NOT FORGET THESE, EITHER!

NEXT MORNING...

ER... EVER HAD THE FEELING THAT SOMETHING'S **MISSING**?

EMPTY!

EEK! **BURGLARS** HAVE STOLEN ALL OUR TROPHIES!

AFTER 'EM!

BUT THEY'LL BE LONG GONE BY NOW!

WRONG, TOMMY! THEY HAVEN'T EVEN MADE IT TO THE **FRONT GATE!**

PANT! WHEEZE!

AND SO...

ALLOW ME TO PRESENT YOU WITH THIS CUP... AWARDED FOR **"THE MOST NOVEL CITIZENS' ARREST"** EVER RECORDED!

BEAM!

SOB!

THERE'S BEEN NO SIGN OF THE EVIL SPIES FOR MONTHS! I WONDER WHAT THEY'RE UP TO?

I'VE GOT A FEELING THAT THEIR SECRET HEADQUARTERS ARE AROUND HERE SOMEWHERE!

EVIL SPIES

EVIL SPIES

NO ENTRY EXCEPT FOR EVIL SPIES!

THIS WAY TO THE EVIL SPIES' SECRET H.Q.

THE EVIL SPIES WELCOME CAREFUL DRIVERS

KEEP OUT SECRET H.Q. AHEAD!

EVIL SPIES' H.Q.

EVIL SPIES H.Q.

THIS MUST BE IT! I'LL PEEK IN AND SEE IF I CAN SEE WHAT THEY'RE DOING!

EVIL SPIES' SECRET H.Q.

PEEKING IN THROUGH THIS WINDOW IS NOT ALLOWED!

HEH, HEH! OUR LATEST PLAN TO TAKE OVER THE WORLD IS WORKING WELL, CHIEF!

IT CERTAINLY IS! OUR FIENDISH ENERGY RAY IS NEARING COMPLETION!

WHEN IT'S FINISHED, NO-ONE WILL BE ABLE TO RESIST US!

THE RAY GETS ITS POWER BY DRAINING ALL THE COLOUR FROM THE WORLD! IT'LL BE READY AS SOON AS EVERY BIT OF COLOUR HAS BEEN REMOVED!

THE VILLAINS! IT'S UP TO ME TO STOP THEM, READER --- AND I'LL NEED YOUR HELP!

BUT HOW CAN I FIND OUT WHERE THE RAY IS BEING BUILT?

BUT, CHIEF--- SUPPOSING SOMEONE FINDS OUT WHERE THE RAY IS BEING BUILT?

IMPOSSIBLE! OUR SECRET MANUFACTURING COMPLEX IS WELL HIDDEN!

THE ONLY WAY TO REACH IT IS THROUGH THE CITY SEWERS, AND EVEN I NEED THIS MAP TO GET TO IT!

CAN YOU HELP ME TO WORK OUT THE ROUTE AND GUIDE ME THROUGH THE SEWERS, READER?

H.Q. START

ABOLISH TUESDAYS

FOLLOW THE MAP AND DECIDE WHETHER THE SECRET COMPLEX IS LOCATED AT A OR B, THEN TURN TO PAGE 47!

10

# MUMMY'S BOY

# IVOR LOTT and TONY BROKE

HI, PENNY! MUM'S SENT ME TO BUY SOME BIN-LINERS!

I'LL TAG ALONG WITH YOU, TONY!

HELLO, YOU SNOBBY PAIR! ARE YOU GOING TO BUY SOME LINERS, TOO?

ONLY ONE, RIFF-RAFF!

ONLY ONE? I'VE BOUGHT A DOZEN!

NOT THAT KIND OF LINER, YOU SILLY COMMONER! FOLLOW US!

AND...

THAT KIND OF LINER!

GASP!

COME ON BOARD AND SEE HOW IMPRESSIVE EVERYTHING IS!

SPEECHLESS!

THE SWIMMING POOL IS SO BIG THAT YOU NEED A BOAT TO GET TO THE OTHER END!

GASP!

AND WE KEEP REAL CROWS IN THE CROWS-NEST!

HOW MANY PASSENGERS CAN THIS LINER CARRY?

PASSENGERS? HOW DARE YOU! I HAVE ONE HALF OF THE SHIP...

...AND I HAVE THE OTHER! WE WOULDN'T HAVE NASTY, COMMON PASSENGERS!

YOU'RE THE CAPTAIN, AREN'T YOU, MY MAN?

THAT'S CORRECT, MASTER IVOR!

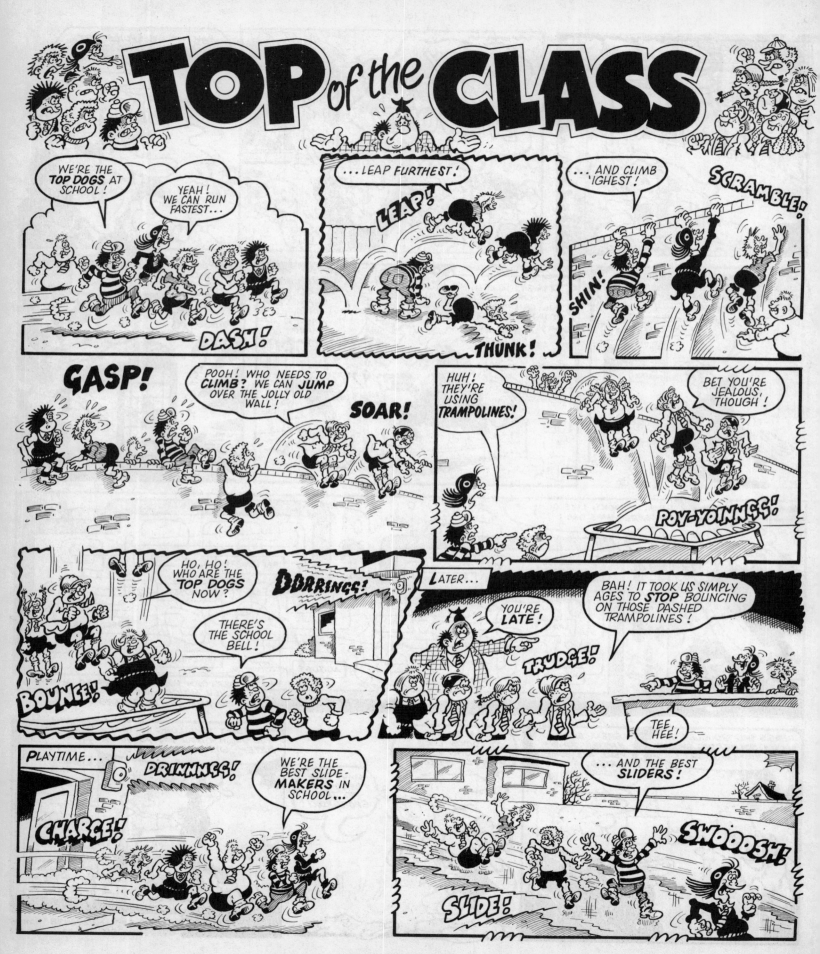

A boy made a brilliant snow figure of his mum, but it melted. "If only I could lose weight so easily," she sighed.

# The Winners

**What did they give the man who invented door knockers?**
The no bell prize!

**Why didn't the two worms go into Noah's ark in an apple?**
Because everyone had to go in pairs.

**In which pantomine does the giant yell: "Fee fi fo fum, I smell the blood of a Scotsman?**
Jock and the Beanstalk!

**Did you hear about the cat who joined the Red Cross?**
It wanted to be a first aid kit!

**Why did the circus fire-eater make headlines?**
His flame had spread!

**What has feathers, fangs and goes quack-quack?**
Count Duckula!

**How do you stop a herd of elephants from charging?**
You take away their credit cards!

**Why was Lassie the most famous dog in films?**
Because she was always given the lead!

**What is a meat thief called?**
A hamburglar!

**Walt's Teasers**

**Knock, knock!**
Who's there?
Dishes.
Dishes who?
**Dishes me. . .whoish you?**

**What's black and white and red all over?**
No, it's not a newspaper – it's a sun-burned zebra!

**What lives underwater and goes da-dit dit-da?**
A morse-cod!

**Why is that dog running in circles?**
It's a watchdog, and it's winding itself up!

**Who runs a disco at school?**
A desk jockey!

**What do you call two turnips who fall in love?**
Swedehearts!

**What did the left eye say to the right eye?**
"There's something between us – and it smells."

**What is a boobee?**
A little bug that runs up the leg of a bee and yells "BOO".

**Why does lightning shock people?**
Because it doesn't know how to conduct itself!

# DRACULA DOBBS

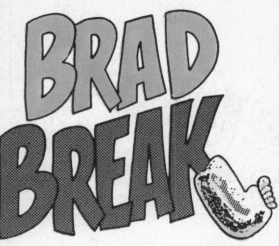

# Puzzle Parade

## The Postman's Problem!

Rearrange each set of jumbled letters to spell the names of six British towns or cities, so that the postman can deliver the parcels to the correct places.

1 WASSEAN
2 RINGHAMBIM
3 PROLOLIVE
4 ROVED
5 TREESCH
6 RIBSLOT

## GET INTO SHAPE!

Which two shapes are the same as each other?

1   2   3   4   5   6   7   8   9

## PETS PUZZLE

Starting at the arrow, move from one square to another — horizontally, vertically, backwards or forwards — to discover the names of five dogs. Remember, use each square only *once!*

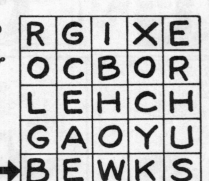

| R | G | I | X | E |
|---|---|---|---|---|
| O | C | B | O | R |
| L | E | H | C | H |
| G | A | O | Y | U |
| → B | E | W | K | S |

## THE PIG IN THE MAZE

Can you lead the pig along the correct path to reach the apple?

## PICTURE PAIRS

There are twenty pictures here which make ten pairs . . . but can you match them up?

41

44

# MUMMY'S BOY

# Melvyn's Mirror

IF YOU PICKED A ON PAGE 10, START READING AT THE ARROW AT THE FOOT OF THE PAGE. IF YOU PICKED B, START READING HERE!

I MADE IT TO THE SEWER EXIT, BUT TIME IS RUNNING OUT! MOST OF THE COLOURS HAVE ALREADY BEEN DRAINED!

THE PLANT MUST BE AROUND HERE, SOMEWHERE! CAN YOU SEE IT, READER?

STUPID READER! NOT THIS SORT OF PLANT--- I MEAN THE MANUFACTURING PLANT WHERE THE EVIL SPIES ARE CONSTRUCTING THEIR ENERGY RAY!

THIS MUST BE IT, BUT HOW AM I GOING TO GET THROUGH THESE SOLID STEEL DOORS?

NO ADMITTANCE by order of THE EVIL SPIES

WH-WHAT'S THAT? A MOUSE!?!

SQUEAK! SQUEAK!

SQUEAK! SQUEAK!

ACME ROBOT CO.

M-MY MISTAKE! IT'S A ROBOT GUARD--- AND IT'S SEEN ME!

QUICK, READER! MAYBE YOU CAN PRESS ONE OF THE BUTTONS ON ITS CHEST!

ABOLISH TUESDAYS

j.edward oliver

WHICH BUTTON WILL YOU PRESS? IF YOU CHOOSE A, USE A PENCIL TO JOIN THE DOTS NUMBERED 1 TO 13 ON THE ROBOT'S CHEST SCREEN. IF YOU PICK B, JOIN THE DOTS LETTERED A TO M! WHEN YOU'VE FINISHED, TURN TO PAGE 81!

A

ARE YOU SURE THIS IS THE RIGHT WAY, READER? IT'S GETTING DARKER AND DARKER, AND---

ROARR!

OOER! S-SOMETHING'S COMING!

H-HELP! IT'S A RUSH OF WATER!

SWOOSH!

YIKES! I'VE BEEN SWEPT OUT TO SEA!

KER-SPLOSH!

WRONG ROUTE, READER! GO BACK TO PAGE 10 AND TRY AGAIN!

A teacher asked for five minutes silence in his class. After a short while a boy piped up:
"How much longer to go, Sir?"

48

# TOP of the CLASS

51

# THUNDERCAP

# The Winners

HEY! I'VE WON A TROMBONE!

THAT'S A FAT LOT OF GOOD! YOU **CAN'T** PLAY THE TROMBONE!

IT JUST SO HAPPENS THAT I CAN PLAY THE FIRST LINE OF "I'VE GOT A LOVELY BUNCH OF COCONUTS"! LISTEN...

WAIT FOR IT!

BLARE!

YEESH! IT'S **HORRIBLE!**

IS THAT THE TELEPHONE RINGING, MUM?

I **DON'T** KNOW! I CAN'T HEAR A THING WITH THAT RACKET GOING ON!

DRING! DRING!

HELLO?... WHAT **DID** YOU SAY?

I'VE GOT TO GO DOWN TO THE TELEVISION STUDIOS!

WHY, MUM?

I DON'T KNOW! I COULDN'T HEAR PROPERLY, THANKS TO YOUR DAD!

WE'LL COME, TOO — ANYTHING TO ESCAPE FROM THAT **ROW!**

AND...

MRS. WINNER! THANK GOODNESS! WE THOUGHT YOU'D FORGOTTEN ABOUT THE SHOW!

TV STUDIO

AND HERE'S MRS. WINNER, TONIGHT'S CONTESTANT ON "NAME THIS SONG"!

OO! I REMEMBER NOW!

IF YOU CAN RECOGNISE THIS SONG FROM THE FIRST FIVE NOTES, YOU WIN TONIGHT'S **STAR PRIZE!**

BLARE!

GAAH! IT'S **THAT** TUNE AGAIN...

..."I'VE GOT A LOVELY BUNCH OF COCONUTS"!

BRILLIANT! AND HERE'S THE PRIZE!

BUT COULD SHE HAVE DONE IT **WITHOUT** DAD'S...ER... HELP?!

# MASTER MIND!

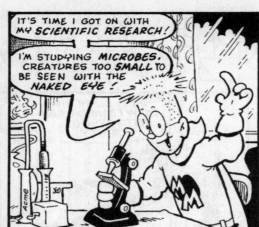

IT'S TIME I GOT ON WITH MY *SCIENTIFIC RESEARCH!*

I'M STUDYING *MICROBES.* CREATURES TOO *SMALL* TO BE SEEN WITH THE *NAKED EYE!*

THERE'S A WHOLE WORLD OF ACTIVITY GOING ON DOWN THERE! TAKE A *LOOK*, READER, AND SEE IF YOU CAN WORK OUT WHAT THE MICROBES ARE *DOING!*

ABOLISH TUESDAYS

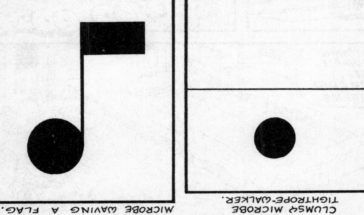

MICROBE WAVING A FLAG.

CLUMSY MICROBE TIGHTROPE-WALKER.

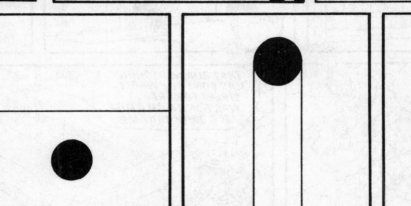

MICROBE ON STILTS.

THREE MICROBES TRYING TO PLAY ONE TRUMPET.

VERY STRONG MICROBE LIFTING AN ELEPHANT.

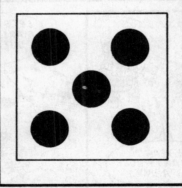

MICROBE STANDING ON A DICE WITH THE "FOUR" SIDE UPWARDS.

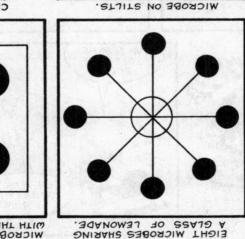

EIGHT MICROBES SHARING A GLASS OF LEMONADE.

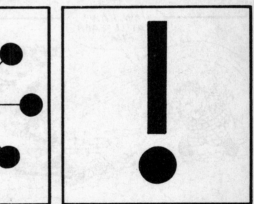

SCOTTISH MICROBE TOSSING THE CABER.

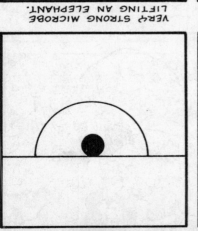

MICROBE WATCHING THE SUNSET.

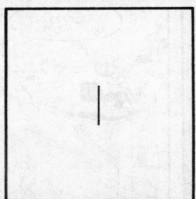

MICROBE THAT'S BEEN ON A DIET.

MICROBES THROWING STONES AT SOMEONE THEY'VE JUST SPOTTED SPYING ON THEM THROUGH A MICROSCOPE.

j.edward oliver

55

# CLEVER DICK

## THE DAFT INVENTOR (AND NAPOLEON DOG)

# X-RAY SPECS

# IVOR LOTT and TONY BROKE

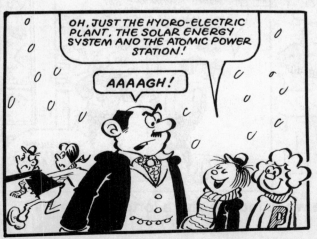

Laugh line: A magician produced two doves, a rabbit, a white mouse and a tortoise from his hat. Then he opened a pet shop.

# Mummy's Boy

73

# It's a Nice Life

And the best of it is— Parky didn't even SEE the JOKE!

# SPORTY

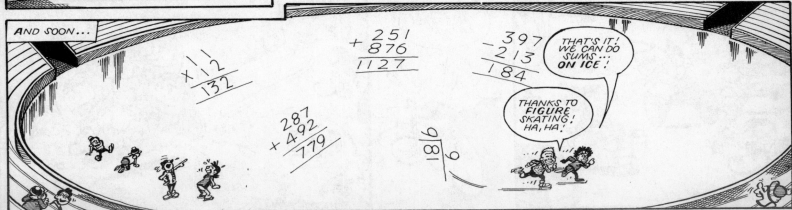

# The Winners

IF YOU GOT THE LETTER "S" WHEN YOU JOINED THE DOTS ON PAGE 47, START READING AT THE ARROW AT THE FOOT OF THE PAGE. IF YOU GOT AN "R", START READING HERE!

GREAT STUFF, READER! YOU'VE PUT THE ROBOT INTO REVERSE!

KERRASH!

YIPPEE! IT'S SMASHED THROUGH THE WALL!

NOW THERE'S NOTHING TO STOP ME GETTING INSIDE THE COMPLEX!

ALL THE COLOUR HAS NOW BEEN DRAINED FROM THE WORLD! THERE CAN ONLY BE SECONDS BEFORE THE EVIL SPIES FIRE THEIR ENERGY RAY! BUT HOW AM I GOING TO FIND IT?

THE ENERGY RAY IS NOT THIS WAY

NOT THIS WAY TO THE ENERGY RAY

NOT THIS WAY, EITHER!

GRROWRR!

Y-YIKES! A G-GUARD DOG!

A

HMMMMM!

B

H-HELP, READER! ONE OF THESE DOORS MUST LEAD TO THE RAY MACHINE--- BUT WHICH ONE ???

ACME WALL CO.

ABOLISH TUESDAYS

WHICH DOOR DO YOU THINK CLIFF SHOULD ENTER? CHOOSE A OR B, THEN USE A PENCIL TO SHADE IN EVERY SPACE THAT CONTAINS A DOT IN YOUR CHOSEN DOOR ONLY! WHEN YOU'VE FINISHED, TURN TO PAGE 103!

j. edward oliver

THE "S" MEANS "STOP"! YOU'VE IMMOBILIZED THE ROBOT, READER---

...BUT YOU MIGHT HAVE GIVEN ME TIME TO GET OUT OF THE WAY, FIRST!

GO BACK TO PAGE 47, RUB OUT YOUR PENCIL LINES AND TRY AGAIN, READER!

The new, improved bus timetable has been a miserable failure. Drivers made themselves late reading it.

At a film studio in Belmonte Village...

OKAY! MAN THE CAMERA! WE'RE ABOUT TO FILM SCENE FIVE OF "DOCTOR FRECKLE AND MR. COWHIDE"!

H'M! THIS LOOKS INTERESTING!

RIGHT! NOW DRINK THE POTION, THEN PULL A **HORRIBLE** FACE AS IF YOU'RE CHANGING INTO "MR. COWHIDE"!

CERTAINLY, DIRECTOR!

HERE GOES!

NOW HE'S GOT TO **PRETEND** TO CHANGE!

GLUG-GLUG!

WHIR-R-R!

AGH-H! UGH! GASP!

M-M! NOT BAD!

HO, HO! VERY GOOD!

SPLUTTER!

WHAT DO YOU MEAN, VERY GOOD? THAT HORRIBLE CONCOCTION WOULD MAKE **ANYBODY** PULL A GHASTLY FACE! IT WAS A **PRUNE** MILK-SHAKE WITH **CURRY POWDER**! I'M **THROUGH**!

HUH! **THAT** WAS CHEAT-ING!

GASP!

GAH! NOW I'VE LOST MY LEADING ACTOR!

...AHEM! I CAN PLAY HIS PART, SIR!

WHAT? DON'T BE SILLY, BOY! WHAT CAN **YOU** DO?

WELL...ER...

...I CAN DO **THIS**!

SCRUNGE!

GASP!

OR, WHAT ABOUT... **THIS**?

SCRUNGE!

A-AGH! GOOD GRIEF!

After the audition...

WHY THE **LONG** FACE? DIDN'T THEY THINK YOU COULD DO THE PART, AFTER ALL?

MY "MR. COWHIDE" WAS FINE...

← Editor's voice

...BUT **THIS** IS MY "DR. FRECKLE" AND NOBODY LIKED IT! I'M NOT GOOD AT **NICE** "SCRUNGES"!

HA, HA! SO WE CAN SEE!

# BEASTENDERS

SO YOU'VE DECIDED TO JOIN IN, AFTER ALL, EH, DAD? BUT YOU SHOULD REALLY DO IT ON A SLEDGE!

BUT...

ERK! THE SNOW'S STICKING TO DAD AND TURNING HIM INTO A GIANT SNOW-BALL!

RUMBLE!

UH-OH!

CRASH!

DAD? ARE YOU ALL RIGHT?

HELP!

LATER:...

WE'RE BACK, MUM!

RECEPTION

GOOD! AND WE HAVE A VISITOR!

MEET AN OLD FRIEND OF MINE WHO'S COME ALL THE WAY FROM THE HIMALAYAS... THE ABOMINABLE SNOWMAN!

HELLO, HERMAN!

I BET YOU'VE NEVER SEEN ANYONE LIKE ME!

YES, I HAVE...

...MEET MY DAD! HEH, HEH!

!!?!!

GASP!

# MUMMY'S BOY

# Puzzle Parade

## CHAIN OF COMMAND!

Arrange the names of these pictured creatures around the circle, so that the *last* letter of each is the *first* letter of the next.

START ► K

## CODE-CRACKLING RIDDLE!

23·8·1·20
19·8·5·5·20
3·1·14·20  2·5
6·15·12·4·5·4?

Each number corresponds with a letter in the alphabet. . .1-A, 2-B etc. Can you solve the message and then answer the riddle?

## 9 ALL

| 3 | 2 | 4 |
|---|---|---|
| 4 | 3 | 2 |
| 3 | 3 | 3 |

Can you place the numbers 2, 3 or 4 in each square, so that all the rows across, down or diagonally add up to 9?

## TV TITLES

Discover the names of three popular television shows in this puzzle by starting at the letter 'G' and following the arrows. (The blank circles are the *spaces* between the words.)

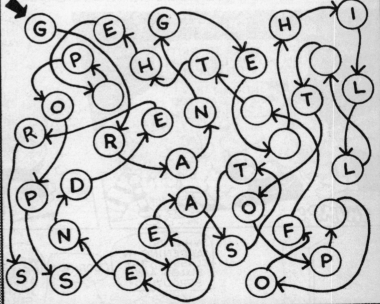

## COUNTRY QUESTIONS!

Milly O'Naire's decided to visit some famous landmarks of the world. Which countries will she have to travel to in order to see the following places?

① THE TAJ MAHAL
② THE ACROPOLIS
③ THE "LEANING TOWER OF PISA"
④ THE STATUE OF LIBERTY
⑤ THE SPHINX
⑥ THE EIFFEL TOWER

## ANSWERS:

*CHAIN OF COMMAND: Kangaroo, ostrich, horse, elephant, tiger, rabbit. CODE RIDDLE: What sheet can't be folded? — A sheet of ice! 9 ALL. 2-4-3...4-3-2...3-2-4. TV TITLES: Grange Hill, Top of the Pops, EastEnders. COUNTRY QUESTIONS: 1. India; 2. Greece; 3. Italy; 4. U.S.A.; 5. Egypt; 6. France.*

# TOP of the CLASS

I HAVE SUGGESTED TO THE HEADMASTER THAT WE COULD START A SCHOOL NEWSPAPER, AND HE HAS GIVEN HIS CONSENT!

A NEWSPAPER! HOW SOOPAH!

HEY! GREAT, TEACH!

WE'LL BE IN THE HEADLINES, OF COURSE... SO COME UP WITH SOME JOLLY GOOD STORIES, CHAPS!

I COULD WRITE ABOUT MY UNCLE... HE'S JUST OFF ON A TRIP UP THE AMAZON!

HOW JOLLY SPIFFING! AND I CAN DO A PIECE ABOUT OUR AFTER-SCHOOL ACTIVITIES!

ENTHUSIASTIC BABBLING!

'OLD ON! WE'RE NOT READIN' A PAPER FULL OF STUFF ABOUT THAT TOFFEE-NOSED LOT!

SNARL! MUTTER!

NO FEAR!

SO COME UP WITH SOME STORIES OF YOUR OWN... THAT'S THE WHOLE IDEA!

YEAH! WE'LL WRITE STORIES ABOUT ALL THE TIMES WE'VE BEATEN THE TOFFS...

...AT EVERYTHIN'!

YEAH! WE'LL BE FAMOUS!

IF YOU DARE TO WRITE UNTRUTHS LIKE THAT YOU'LL BE FOR IT!

INDUBITABLY! WE CAN SUE YOU FOR LIBEL!

OH, YEAH?

SPLUTTERING OUTRAGE!

THUMP!

NO, NO! WE DON'T WANT ANY STORIES ABOUT FIGHTING OR ARGY-BARGY!

AW! BUT THAT'S WHAT WE'RE BEST AT!

STARTING TO WONDER IF THIS WAS SUCH A GOOD IDEA!

WE JUST WANT STORIES AND INFORMATION ABOUT THE THINGS THAT ARE GOING ON IN CLASS...

DESPERATE ENTHUSIASM!

!?

WHAT IS 'APPENING IN CLASS?... THE BULBS ARE SPROUTING!

BORING!

WE'LL WRITE ABOUT THAT, SIR!

LESS THAN THRILLED!

NO! WE'LL WRITE ABOUT IT! MY EAGLE-LIKE REPORTER'S EYE SPOTTED IT FIRST!

GIVE ME THAT, YOU SCRUFF!

GRAB!

SNATCH!

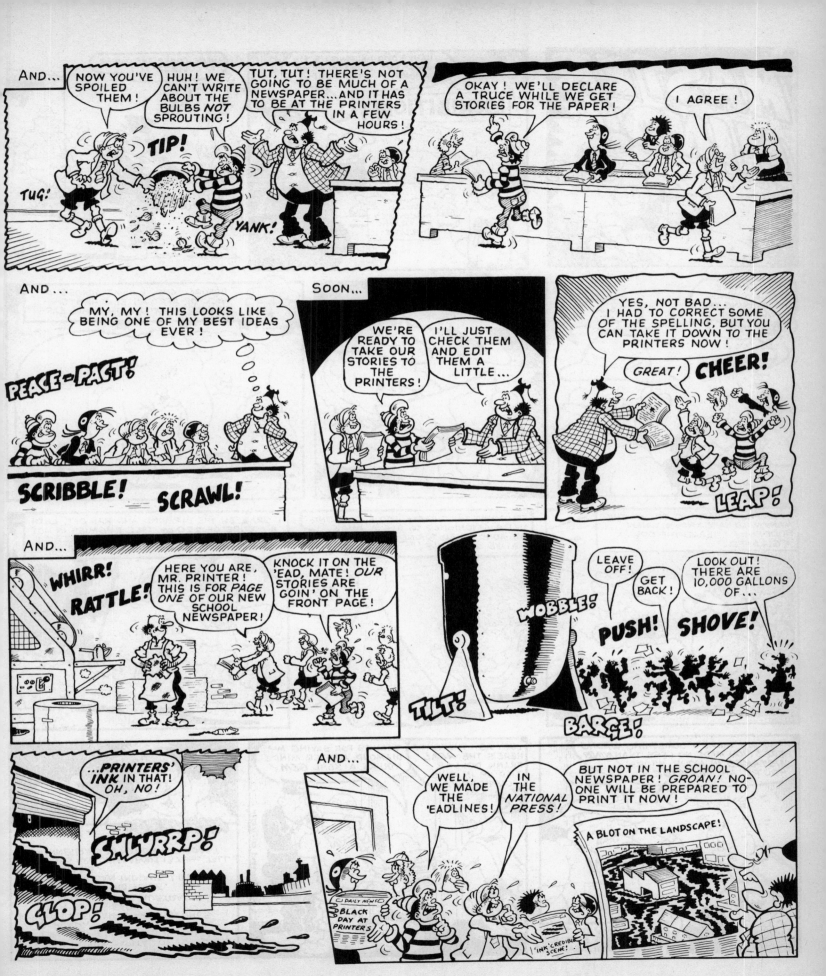

# IVOR LOTT and TONY BROKE
## with MILLY O'NAIRE and PENNY LESS

NEWSAGENT

I'VE BOUGHT A NEW PENCIL FOR THE NEW SCHOOL TERM!

AND I'VE BOUGHT A NEW NOTEBOOK!

AGENT

WE'RE READY FOR ANYTHING NOW!

WELL! SO RIFF-RAFF CAN ACTUALLY READ AND WRITE!

OR MAYBE THEY JUST DRAW LITTLE PICTURES!

YOU MEAN YOU'VE NOT GOT ANY PENCILS AND BOOKS?

OH, DEARIE-ME, NO! THE VERY IDEA!

WE'VE BOUGHT THOSE NEW WORD-PROCESSING MACHINES INSTEAD!

COO! WHERE ARE THEY TAKING THEM?

THEY'RE GOING TO OUR DESKS RIGHT AT THE TOP OF THE BUILDING!

WOW!

SCHOOL

JUST A MINUTE! HOW DO THEY KNOW WHICH WILL BE YOUR DESKS?

SILLY...

...WE BRING OUR OWN!

I'VE JUST REMEMBERED, I HAVE TO BUY A NEW SCHOOL TIE!

AND I HAVE TO GET SOME SOCKS!

# Melvyn's Mirror

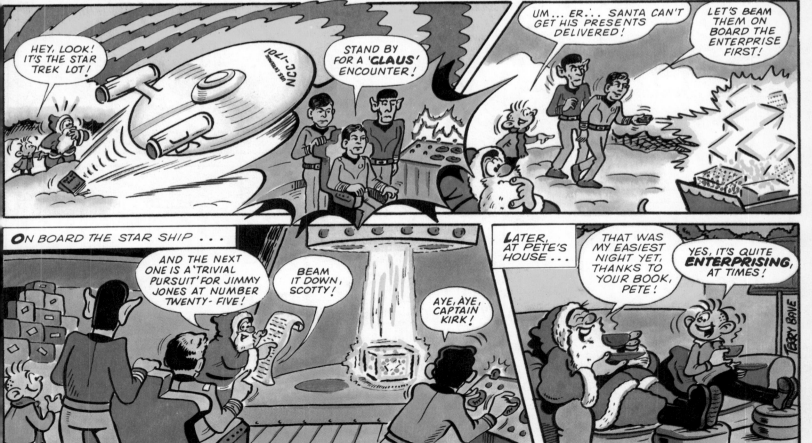

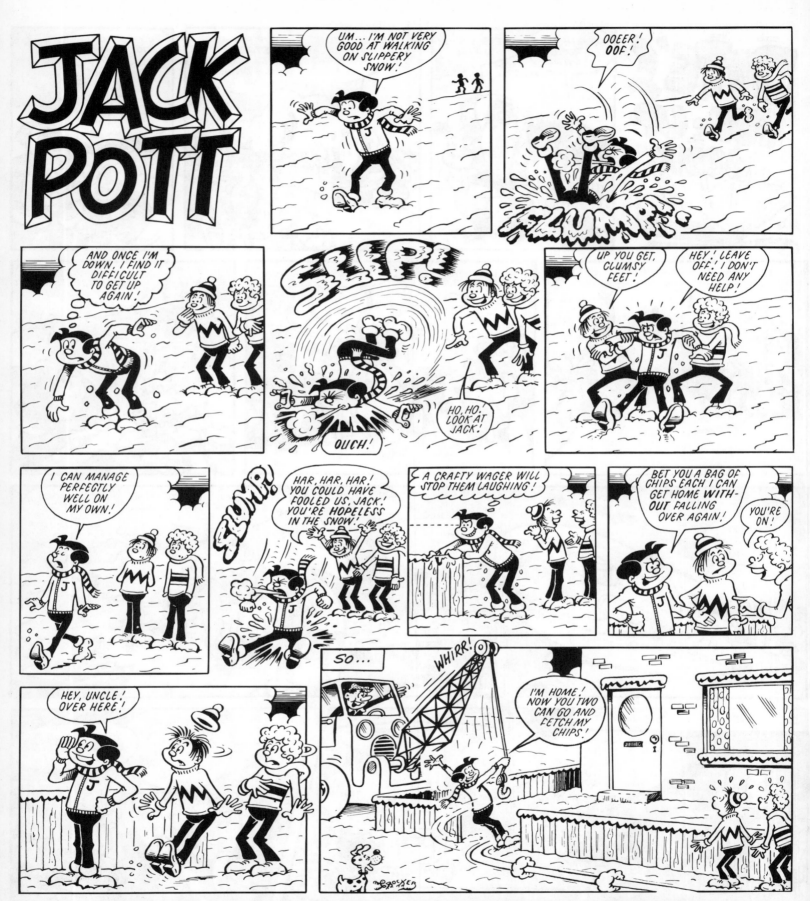

**Thieves who stole a lorry load of bananas skidded and crashed after a high-speed police chase. A spokesman said they'd slipped up badly.**

IF YOU PICKED DOOR A ON PAGE 81, START READING *HERE!* IF YOU CHOSE DOOR B, BEGIN READING AT THE ARROW MARKED "B" BELOW!

HOORAY! YOU'VE FOUND THE RAY MACHINE, READER!

RRROWWF! SNAP!

THERE'S ONLY ONE PROBLEM--- UP HERE, I'M SAFE FROM THE DOG, BUT I CAN'T REACH THE CONTROLS!

TURN BACK TO PAGE 81 AND TRY THE OTHER DOOR!

OOER! IT'S A B-BEEHIVE! THIS MUST BE WHERE THE EVIL SPIES MAKE THEIR OWN HONEY!

HMMMM!

THE BEES LOOK ANGRY! I'LL SWING UP HERE, OUT OF THE WAY---

BZZZZZ!

---AND THEY CAN CHASE AWAY THE GUARD DOG!

BZZZZZ!

HERE'S THE RAY MACHINE, NEXT DOOR! IT'S ALREADY WARMING UP, B-BUT THE MASTER SWITCH SEEMS TO BE A MATHEMATICAL COMBINATION!

THRMMMM!

$1 + 1 = 10$

ABOLISH TUESDAYS

MASTER SWITCH INSTRUCTIONS: REMOVE TWO OF THE VERTICAL BARS TO MAKE THE SUM CORRECT!

$$\underset{A}{|} + \underset{B}{|} = \underset{C}{|} \underset{D}{|} 0$$

HURRY, READER! WHICH TWO BARS SHALL I REMOVE?

MAKE YOUR CHOICE BEFORE READING ON!

REMOVING BARS B AND D LEAVES THE CORRECT SUM: $1 - 1 = 0$

IT WORKED---AND JUST IN THE NICK OF TIME! ALL THE COLOUR HAS BEEN RESTORED

THRMMMPHUT!

WHAT'S GOING ON? WHY HASN'T THE RAY FIRED?

IT'S THAT BRAT, CLIFF HANGER! GRAB HIM

CAN YOU SUGGEST A WAY FOR CLIFF TO SAVE HIMSELF, READER?

GOOD THINKING, READER! THE HONEY!!

SLURP!

HO, HO! THAT'LL MAKE THEM STICK AROUND UNTIL THE POLICE GET HERE!

WELL DONE, READER! YOU'VE SAVED ME FROM A STICKY SITUATION!

THE END!

# Buster

# X-RAY SPECS

# FACEACHE

Lunchtime at "Belmonte" school...

You shouldn't gulp your lemonade, Faceache! You'll give yourself hiccups and you know what will happen then!

GLUG-GLUG!

And, it did...

HIC!

SCRUNGE!

HIC!

SCRUNGE!

Snipe will be furious if you start "scrunging" in class this afternoon!

M-M-M! He's right! But I know what I can do...HIC! Whoops! There I go AGAIN!

SCRUN-NGE!

Shortly, in the pottery class...

I've made a mask of my own face from pulped paper! Snipe won't know I'm scrunging when I wear it...HIC!

SCRUNGE!

That afternoon...

A-hem! The capital of France is...

HIC! HIC!

SCRUNGE!

Faceache! Stop making those STUPID noises!

'Sorry, sir! I've hiccups...HIC!

SCRUNGE!

Well, get a drink of water, and remember—NO "scrunging". Or else!

Don't worry, sir! You won't see me "scrunging" today!

In the washroom...

I'll have a drink from this press-button fountain... GLUG-GLUG-GLUG!

SPLAT!

CLUMP! CLUMP!

Have you got rid of your...A-AGH! You've done it AGAIN!

Eh? Done what?

"Scrunged" you fiend! And you're going to write 5,000 times after school, "I must not defy authority"!

B-BUT...

Back in the classroom, Faceache discovered the horrible TRUTH...

Bah! I can't win! The water SOFTENED my paper mask and caused it to sag— making me look like THIS!

SOGGY

108

# The Winners